Share Your Life's Journey With Me, Dad

A GUIDED JOURNAL AND MEMORY KEEPSAKE

Scat Cat Publishing

This Book Belongs To

_____

Table of Contents

This journal is a canvas for Dads to paint their life stories. As you reflect on your experiences, from joyful moments to profound wisdom, know that each memory you record is a precious gift to your family.

Why share your story? Because your life's unique tapestry offers invaluable lessons and cherished stories that illuminate the paths of those who follow.

This journal invites you to celebrate your journey, reconnect with past joys, and preserve these moments for generations to cherish.

Thank you for sharing your heart and your journey.

Chapter One:
Birth

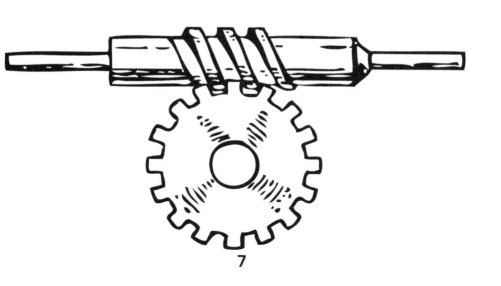

Birth

Dad, share with me what day and year you were born. What time your were born and where your were born!

_____

_____

_____

_____

_____

_____

_____

_____

_____

_____

_____

_____

_____

_____

_____

What color was your hair at birth?

What color were your eyes?

How much did you weigh at birth?

Were you a healthy baby?

Did you suck your thumb?

attach your baby
picture here

Additional Journaling Space

Chapter Two: Early Years

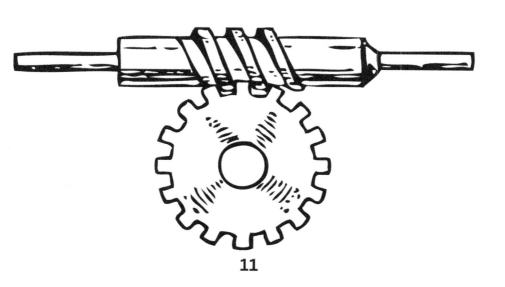

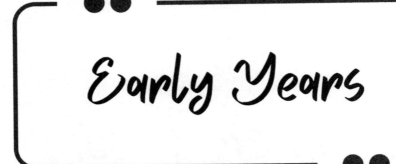

Early Years

Dad, tell me about your family growing up. Did you have siblings, cousins or were you an only child?

_____
_____
_____
_____
_____
_____
_____
_____

What quirky habits did you have as a child?

_____
_____
_____
_____
_____
_____

Did you have a favorite toy? Or what about a pet? What was the toy or pets name?

What is one of you favorite stories from your early childhood?

Describe a typical family meal from your childhood?

What traditions did your family have? Have you continued any in your own family?

Did you attend church with your family? What denomination are you? Were you baptized as an infant or young boy?

Were you raised in the same house all your life?

Describe a favorite family vacation or outing you remember from your childhood.

Did you have a favorite book or story as a child? What was it?

What was the first major news event your remember living through?

Can you recall a particularly funny or embarrassing moment from your school days?

What was your favorite subject(s) in school? What did you like about them?

What school subject(s) did you find most difficult?

Who was your favorite elementary teacher and why?

Who was your best friend in
elementary school? Do you still keep
in touch?

What was your favorite childhood
game to play?

What music did you love as a young
boy, and what was your favorite
band or song?

Additional Journaling Space

Chapter Three: Teen Years

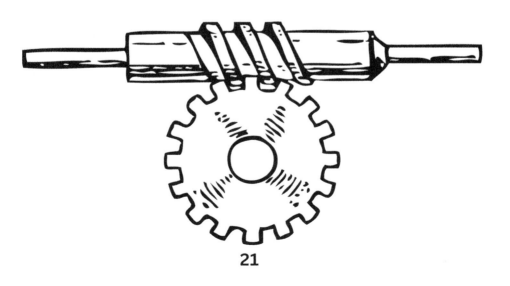

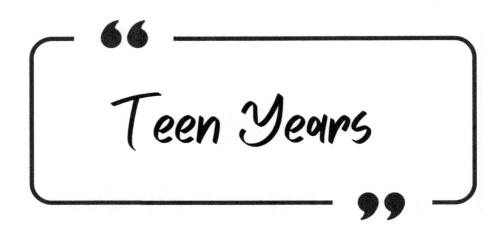

Dad, what were your teenage years
like? Describe a typical day.

_____
_____
_____
_____
_____
_____
_____

How did you spend your summers
as a teenager?

_____
_____
_____
_____
_____

What fashion trend did you love
most during your youth?

How old were you when you started
shaving?

Have you ever won any awards or
competitions? What were they for?

What kind of student were you in
high school?

What was your first concert like?
Who did you see?

Who was the first person you ever
kissed? How old were you?

How did you meet your best friend,
and are you still in touch?

What was the biggest trouble you
got into as a teenager?

How did your parents discipline you,
and what do you think of it now?

What was your first job, and what
did you learn from it?

Describe your first car - what kind
was it and where did you go with it?

What was one of the biggest
challenges you faced as a teenager?

What music did you love as a
teenager, and what was your
favorite band or song?

Additional Journaling Space

Chapter Four:

Adult Years

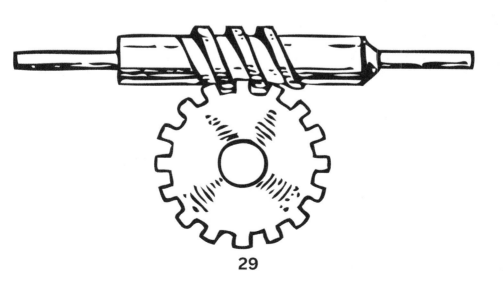

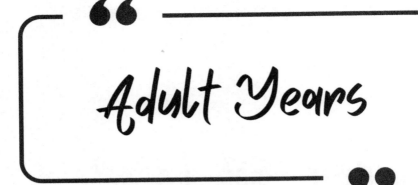

Adult Years

Dad, briefly describe your 20's using the prompts to help you.

How did you celebrate turning 21?

Reflecting on your time as a young man in your twenties, what were some of the most significant challenges and joys you encountered? How did these experiences shape your approach to parenting?

How did you manage to balance
your personal aspirations with your
responsibilities as a young dad?
What were some of your personal
goals at the time, and how did you
strive to achieve them?

Looking back, what hopes did you
have for your children during those
early years, and how did you work
towards supporting their dreams?

Dad, briefly describe your 30's using
the prompts to help you.

As you look back on your 30's, what
were the pivotal moments that
defined that decade for you?

How did your perspective on family
and relationships evolve during your
30's?

What major life goals did you accomplish in your 30's, and what impact did these achievements have on your personal and professional life?

Dad, briefly describe your 40's using the prompts to help you.

What were some of the most
challenging and rewarding
experiences you faced in your 40's?

Reflecting on your 40's, how did your priorities change during this period compared to your earlier years?

How did you manage the balance between career advancement and family life during this busy decade?

Dad, briefly describe your 50's using the prompts to help you.

During your 50's, what steps did you take to prepare for the later years in terms of health, finance, or personal hobbies?

How did your relationships with friends and family deepen or change in your 50's?

Looking back at your 50's, what wisdom did you gain that was different from earlier in your life?

Dad, briefly describe your 60's using the prompts to help you.

Reflecting on your 60's, what are you most proud of achieving or experiencing during this decade?

What advice would you give to someone about to enter their 60's based on your own experiences?

How have you adjusted to any lifestyle changes that came with this stage of life, such as retirement or changes in physical activity?

What do you believe is the key to a happy life?

Do you golf? What's your handicap?

Dad, briefly describe your 70's using the prompts to help you.

Reflecting on your 70s, how has your relationship with your grandchildren enriched your life? What unique experiences have you shared with them?

What traditions have you started or continued with your grandchildren that you hope they'll remember fondly?

What are the benefits of getting older?

What was your favorite age and why?

What changes have you seen in the world that surprise you?

Spouse

Dad, how did you meet your spouse and what was your first impression?

_____
_____
_____
_____

How long did you date before you proposed to your spouse?

_____
_____
_____

Where did you propose to your spouse at?

_____
_____
_____

Describe your wedding day or a significant moment in your relationship with your spouse.

How old were you when you got married?

What was your wedding song and why did you choose it?

What is one of your fondest
memories from the early days of
your marriage?

How have you and your spouse
managed to grow together over the
years?

What's something you've learned
about love and relationships?

Fatherhood

Dad, what were your hopes and dreams when you first became a parent?

What was your reaction when your spouse told you, you were going to be a father?

What was the most surprising thing
about fatherhood?

How did becoming a father change
you?

Were you a working father or a stay at home dad?

What did you find most challenging about raising children?

Describe a moment when you felt
really proud of your family.

How do you feel about your
children's parenting styles?

Describe a family tradition you hope your children will continue.

What's your most memorable moment as a father?

What advice would you give someone about to become a parent?

Were you active in a church?

Did you volunteer at your child's school?

Join PTA?

Substitute teach?

Coach any sports your child was involved in?

If you had to rate yourself as a
parent what score would you give
yourself? Circle a number.

0 1 2 3 4 5 6 7 8 9 10

Explain why?

What has fatherhood taught you
about yourself?

What is the best advice your
mother or father ever you?

Did you take it?   Yes or No Why?

What's the hardest part of being a
father?

Were you adopted?

Who are your birth parents? Have
you met them?

Do you have any biological siblings,
and if so, who are they? Where do
they live?

Additional Journaling Space

Additional Journaling Space

Chapter Five:
Genealogy

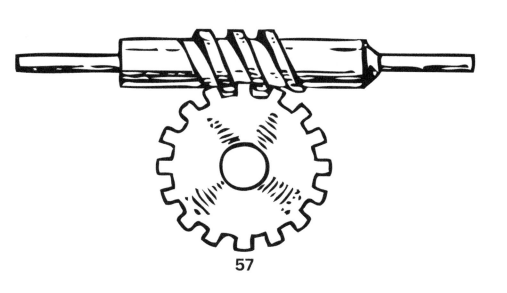

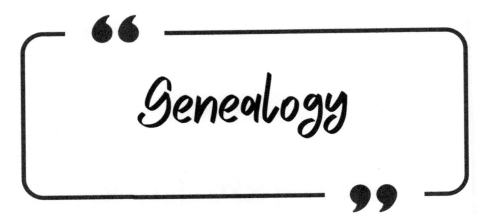

Genealogy

Dad, where did you come from?
Please share what you can about your
family genealogy.

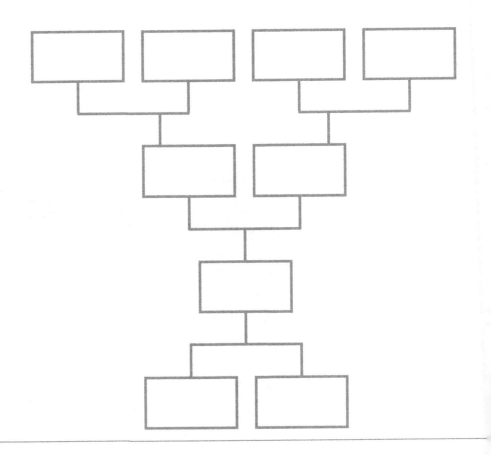

Genealogy

Provide your great grandparents
name, DOB and death:

Provide your grandparents, and
DOB and death:

Provide your parents name, DOB
and death:

Provide your birth name and DOB:

Share what you know about your ancestry.

Was there anyone famous in your family ancestry?

What country did your family immigrate from?

Have you ever visited the country where your ancestors originated from and met your relatives there?

Additional Journaling Space

Additional Journaling Space

Chapter Six: Relationships

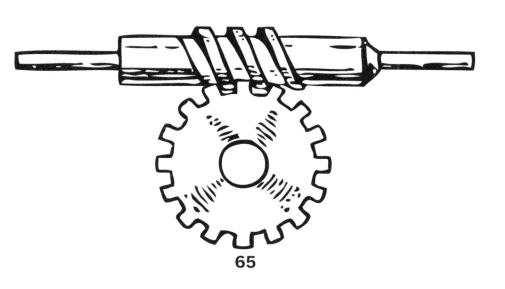

Relationships

Dad, how has your relationship with your siblings evolved over the years?

_____
_____
_____
_____
_____
_____
_____
_____

Who are the most influential people in your life and why?

_____
_____
_____
_____
_____
_____
_____

Describe a perfect day spent with friends.

What advice would you give about maintaining friendships?

What do you cherish most about our family?

What are your hopes for your children and grandchildren?

What lessons do you hope to pass on about marriage?

What's the most important thing you've taught your children?

What values are most important to you?

Chapter Seven:
Memorable
Milestones

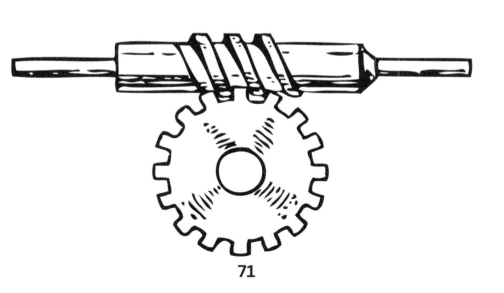

"Memorable Milestones"

Dad, you've achieved so much throughout your life. Could you share some of your most memorable moments? Please highlight significant events from your childhood to adulthood.

What was an unexpected opportunity that you seized in your life, and how did it turn out?

Can you tell us about a moment of serendipity that brought an unexpected joy or success?

Which personal challenge did you overcome that you initially thought was insurmountable?

Have there been any cultural or historical events during your lifetime that deeply influenced or changed you? How did you respond at the time?

Chapter Eight:
Trials & Triumphs

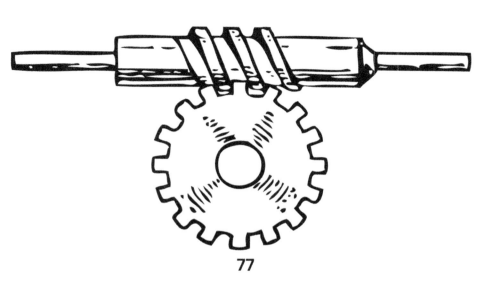

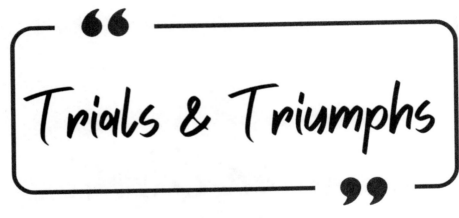

Trials & Triumphs

Dad, please share the challenges
you've faced and overcome, along
with the victories that have shaped
who you are.

_____
_____
_____
_____
_____
_____
_____
_____
_____
_____
_____
_____
_____
_____
_____
_____
_____
_____

Is there a specific achievement or victory that you feel defines your character? How so?

Looking back, which challenge taught you the most about yourself?

What was one of the most difficult
periods in your life, and how did you
manage to overcome it?

Can you share a victory that came from a particularly challenging situation?

Chapter Nine:
Beliefs & Values

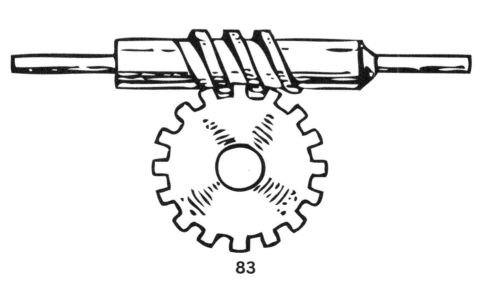

Beliefs & Values

Dad, reflect on the principles that have guided your life's decisions.

Provide a favorite bible or life verse.

What core values have you always held dear, and how have they influenced the decisions you make?

Is there a particular life lesson or piece of advice you received that has profoundly shaped your approach to life's decisions?

Can you describe a time when
sticking to your principles was
particularly challenging, but
ultimately rewarding?

How have your guiding principles evolved over your lifetime?

Chapter Ten:
Wisdom & Insights

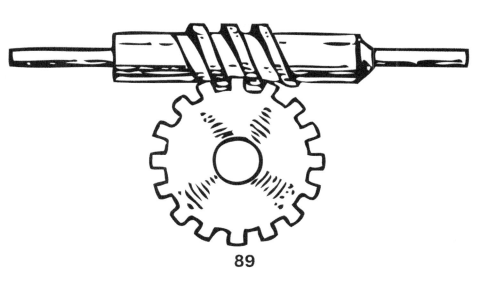

" Wisdom & Insights "

Dad, share your life lessons learned
and wisdom gained over the years.

Looking back, what advice would
you give to your younger self based
on the wisdom you have now?

What is the most important life
lesson you've learned, and who
taught it to you?

What is one mistake you made and
the lesson you learned from it?

Chapter Eleven: Dreams & Aspirations

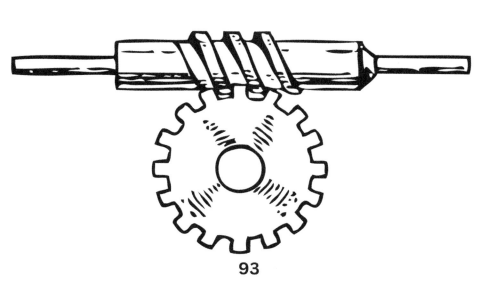

Dreams & Aspirations

Dad, share your past dreams and future hopes for yourself and your family.

Can you share a dream that you have successfully achieved? How did it feel to accomplish it?

What is one dream that you haven't
yet fulfilled, but still hope to achieve?

Looking to the future, what are your
hopes for your own life in the coming
years?

What is one dream that you haven't yet fulfilled, but still hope to achieve?

What are your greatest hopes and
wishes for your family's future?

How do you envision the legacy
you'd like to leave for your children
and grandchildren?

Chapter Twelve: Reflections

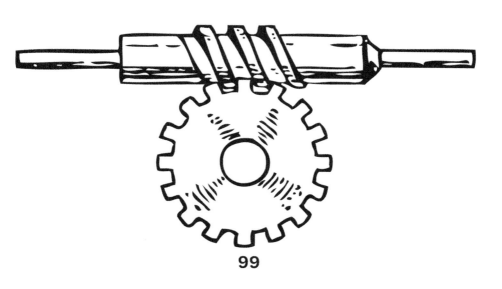

Reflections

Dad, you are a true gem to our family. What invaluable advice would you like to pass on?

How do you want to be remembered by friends and family?

What are your hopes for your children and grandchildren?

What message do you have for future generations of our family?

How do you want to celebrate major milestones?

What's the most valuable family heirloom you possess?

What achievement(s) are you most
proud of?

What was a turning point in your life,
and why was it significant?

What do you believe about the
nature of happiness?

What are your thoughts on
spirituality and religion?

Do you believe in God? Are you
saved?

Things I Hope To Teach My Children

Dad, what wisdom would you like to pass on to us?

How do you approach learning new things?

What life lessons did you learn the hard way?

Chapter Thirteen: Military Service

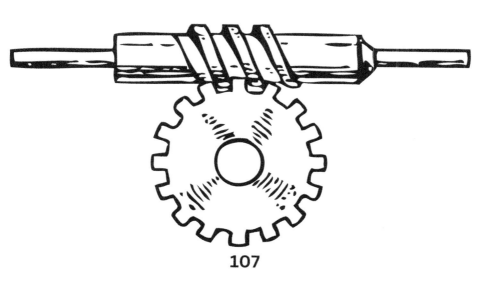

Dad, share with us your military experience.

How old were you when you joined the military?

Why did you decide to join the military?

What branch did you serve in?
Why did you choose this branch?

Did you join the military to continue a family tradition? If so, which family member inspired this path?

What was your job or role in the military?

Did you receive any special
training? What was it like?

How many years did you serve?

Did you travel to other countries because of your military service? Where did you go?

What was the hardest part about being in the military?

What was a typical day like for you in the military?

What military figure did you most look up to in your life? Why?

Which President was in office during your time in the service?

Did you respect his military decisions?

What are some of your most
memorable experiences from your
time in service?

Did you graduate from a military
academy? If so which one?

What was your discharge status
when you left the military?

Did you operate any specific machinery or equipment during your military service, such as piloting an aircraft?

Did you make any close friends while serving? Can you tell me about them?

Did you sustain any injuries while serving?

What advice would you give to someone thinking about joining the military?

Looking back, if you had to do it all over again would you still enlist?

Chapter Fourteen: Fun & Quirky

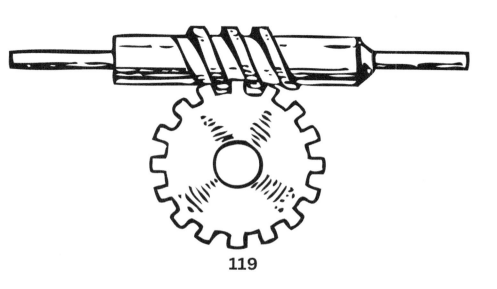

Fun & Quirky

Dad, I bet your hand is hurting by now writing so much in the previous pages. Let's have some fun now.

What's your favorite color?

What's your favorite animal?

What's your favorite season?

What's your guilty pleasure ?

What's your favorite cocktail ?

What's your favorite, beer or wine?

If you could have any superpower, what would it be and why?

Did you ever smoke Marijuana?

What's the strangest food you ever tried and did you like it?

Which celebrity did you have a crush on as a teenager?

If you could be any animal for a day, which one would you choose?

What's the funniest prank you've ever pulled on someone?

What song always gets you out on the dance floor?

If you could live in any TV show, which one would it be?

What's the most unusual thing you have in your wallet right now?

If you had to eat only one food for the rest of your life, what would it be?

What's your secret talent that not many people know about?

If you could travel back in time, which decade would you visit and why?

What's the silliest thing you are
afraid of?

If you could invite three famous
people (dead or alive) to dinner, who
would they be?

What's the best piece of advice you
ever ignored?

What was your most memorable
Halloween costume?

If you could instantly become an expert in something, what would it be?

What's the most bizarre thing you've ever read or seen on the internet?

What is one thing you tried as a child and vowed never to do again?

If you were a character in a book, what type of character would you be?

Looking back, what was the most dangerous thing you ever did that didn't seem dangerous at the time?

Did you go to College? What did you major in? Were you in a fraternity?

How old were you when you got your first tattoo? What was it?

Democrat or Republican?

Recipes

Dad, could you share some of your favorite family recipes with us? We'd love to have them as a way to remember you.

What's the best piece of cooking advice you ever received?

What's your favorite protein to grill?

Do you consider yourself a good cook? Griller?

Additional Journaling Space

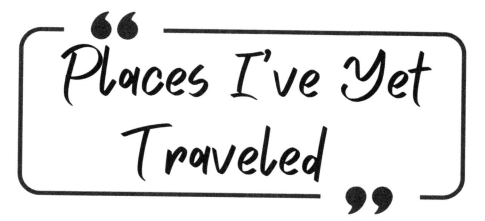

Places I've Yet Traveled

Dad, share with us places you'd like to travel to.

Additional Journaling Space

Dad, I hope you've found joy and enlightenment in preserving these memories for your family. It's a great way to celebrate all the moments that have shaped you.

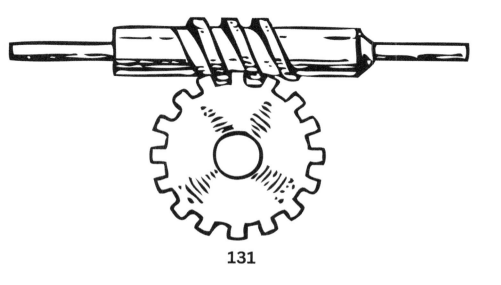

Heartfelt Request: Your Review Matters

Dear Reader,

Thank you for choosing the "Share Your Life's Journey With, Me" book. We hope this guided journal enriches your loved ones' journey and provides inspiration and guidance in sharing their unique life story.

If you've found this book valuable, we would greatly appreciate it if you could take a moment to share your thoughts in an Amazon review. Your feedback not only helps us refine future editions but also aids other readers in finding the right book to meet their needs.

How to Share Your Review:
Simply scan the QR code below to visit the book's Amazon page and leave your review. Your input will help fellow readers discover this series and the joy it brings.

Thank you for being a part of this journey with us. Your review means the world to us and makes a positive impact on our work!

Warmest regards, Scat Cat Publishing

Printed in Great Britain
by Amazon